Reading
FOR CONTENT

Carol Einstein

Book 2

Educators Publishing Service, Inc.
Cambridge and Toronto

I would like to thank my husband, Hans Neukomm,
and my son, Robert Neukomm, for their unfailing
support and encouragement.

Educators Publishing Service, Inc.

31 Smith Place, Cambridge, Massachusetts 02138-1000

March, 1997 Printing

Table of Contents   Page

Introduction for the Teacher

The *Reading for Content* series is designed to help improve students' reading comprehension skills at various levels Four comprehension questions accompany each passage. Questions one and two are main idea questions, and questions three and four are conclusion questions. Students should circle the letter of the correct answer. The answer sheet and progress graph on pages 88-91 are important aspects of the book. Students can see the types of errors they are making, and the teacher can give needed help. Filling in the progress graph in the back allows students to record and chart their progress.

Directions for Students

1. Read the passage.
2. Answer the questions. Do all the questions that you know first. Then go back and try to answer the questions that you left out. If you are not sure of an answer, it will be helpful to reread the passage to find the answer to the question.
3. Correct your answers with the answer key. Plot your comprehension score on the progress graph.

Passage 1

There is a growing interest in old railroad cars. These old cars remind people of other times. Years ago train travel was lots of fun. From the late 1800s to the mid-1950s some railroad cars were very beautiful and very comfortable, too. This kind of travel ended when people started to use planes.

Today these old cars are being put to new use. They have been turned into ice cream parlors, snack bars, and shops. The cars are also used for special rides.

At a sale of old railroad cars one couple said they planned to make a car into a fancy store. They would sell sandwiches and pizzas in it. Another person wanted a domed car with a skylight to use as a classroom for studying the stars. The mayor of a town wanted to buy a car because it had her town's name on it.

The prices of railroad cars vary. Generally, a car costs between $5,000 and $15,000. However, a car in very poor condition, fit only for scrap iron, costs a few thousand dollars while a car in good condition with a domed roof could cost up to $150,000.

1. Choose the best title.
    a. Trains
    b. Buying a New Railroad Car
    c. A New Interest in Old Railroad Cars
    d. Train Travel

2. Choose the best answer.
   Old railroad cars can be used
    a. as restaurants.
    b. as shops.
    c. as motels.
    d. in many different ways.

3. Trains became less popular because
    a. airplanes were faster.
    b. airplanes were safer.
    c. it took more time to get to railroad stations than to airports.
    d. it took less time to get to airports than to railroad stations.

4. We can conclude that if a railroad car costs $21,000, it must be
    a. in good condition.
    b. in fair condition.
    c. in excellent condition.
    d. in poor condition.

Passage 2

Charles Lindbergh made the first solo, non-stop airplane flight across the Atlantic Ocean. He left New York City on the morning of May 20, 1927 and landed in Paris the next night. The trip was 3,600 miles and took 33 hours and 30 minutes.

Lindbergh had to keep the airplane light since he needed a lot of gas. Thus he took only five sandwiches and a quart of water with him. All over the world people were listening to radios and reading newspapers. They were hoping Lindbergh would get to Paris safely.

When his small, one-engine airplane landed, more than 100,000 people were waiting in Paris. Foreign countries gave him medals.

When Lindbergh came back to the United States, President Coolidge welcomed him and gave him the Distinguished Flying Cross. Millions of people honored him. Lindbergh was only 25 years old, but he was a hero of the world.

Because people in St. Louis, Missouri gave Lindbergh money to have his plane built, he named it *The Spirit of St. Louis*. The plane is now in the National Air and Space Museum in Washington, D.C.

Passage 2

1. Choose the best answer.
   Lindbergh's Atlantic flight was the first flight made
   a. non-stop.
   b. alone.
   c. alone and non-stop.
   d. in such a short time.

2. Choose the best answer.
   Which people hoped Lindbergh would get to Paris?
   a. people in the United States
   b. people in St. Louis
   c. people in France
   d. people in many countries

3. We can guess that after Lindbergh's flight people
   a. were more afraid to fly across the ocean.
   b. were less afraid to fly across the ocean.
   c. thought he was a foolish show-off.
   d. forgot about him.

4. Which city first supported Lindbergh?
   a. New York
   b. Paris
   c. St. Louis
   d. Washington

Passage 3

The Hardy Boys and the Nancy Drew series were written by Harriet Adams. Both series had been started by her father in the late 1920s. After he died in 1930, his daughter continued writing these books. She used a different name when she wrote each series. She wrote The Hardy Boys under the name of Franklin Dixon. The Nancy Drew stories were written under the name of Carolyn Keene.

Mrs. Adams wrote more than 50 books for each series. It took her only six to eight weeks to write each book. She also rewrote many of the earlier books. She did this to bring them up-to-date.

Why are these books so well-liked? Why have millions of them been sold?

Many of her books have spooky themes and secrets. Her characters do things readers themselves would like to do. The action often takes place at a circus, a parade, or a fair.

The books are very true to life. The events could really have taken place. All of her characters are interesting, and each one contributes to the action of the story.

1. Mrs. Adams' books are popular because
   a. the plots are exciting.
   b. the stories are funny.
   c. they are new books.
   d. she writes only about sports.

2. According to this passage which sentence is true?
   a. The Hardy Boys are more popular than the Nancy Drew books.
   b. Mrs. Adams was the first person to write The Hardy Boys.
   c. There are about 30 books in each series.
   d. The Hardy Boys and the Nancy Drew books are both old series.

3. Choose the best answer.
   If Mrs. Adams had written a new series, she might have used the name
   a. Harriet Keene.
   b. Carolyn Keene.
   c. William Jackson.
   d. Franklin Dixon.

4. From this passage we can conclude that Mrs. Adams
   a. had a good imagination.
   b. spent little time on writing.
   c. knew little about children.
   d. liked animals.

Passage 4

Besides the gorilla and the chimpanzee there are two other interesting apes: the gibbon and the orangutan.

The gibbon, the smallest of the apes, is thin. This ape weighs about 15 pounds and is about three feet tall. Its coat is brown or black or gray.

Gibbons live in trees, using their long arms to help them go from branch to branch. They move very quickly. They hold on to the branches with their fingers, and they swing back and forth like acrobats. They can leap into the air and jump long distances.

The orangutan is a large ape with long, reddish-brown hair. Its name comes from a Malay word meaning "man of woods." These apes are ugly but smart. Their faces are flat with swollen cheeks. When standing, adult males are about four feet high. They weigh between 150 and 200 pounds, but females are smaller.

Orangutans have extremely long arms. These long arms help them move along the branches of trees.

They build nests or beds from 20 to 80 feet above the ground. They like to live in trees and do not come down to the ground often.

Passage 4

1. Compared to the orangutan the gibbon is
   a. much smaller.
   b. somewhat smaller.
   c. larger.
   d. much larger.

2. Both of these apes spend most of their time
   a. on the ground.
   b. in tree trunks.
   c. on tree branches.
   d. on rocks.

3. Which is most useful to the gibbon and the orangutan?
   a. their arms
   b. their legs
   c. their feet
   d. their eyes

4. From this passage we can conclude that orangutans are like birds because they
   a. go south in the winter.
   b. build nests in trees.
   c. are pretty.
   d. take care of their young.

Passage 5

Some people love roller coaster rides because they get thrills and fun from them. Other people couldn't be dragged on to a roller coaster.

Roller coasters are made of wood or metal. The old-fashioned roller coasters were wooden. Metal ones were developed more recently.

The old wooden roller coasters looked and sounded as though they might break apart. As they climbed, the riders heard creaking sounds. They became dizzy and terrified by the fast loops and turns through the air and the sharp, long plunge to the ground.

One of the oldest wooden roller coasters is the Cyclone, in Coney Island, New York. In 1927, Charles Lindbergh flew across the Atlantic Ocean, and shortly after, he rode on the Cyclone. He said, "A ride on the Cyclone is a greater thrill than flying an airplane at top speed."

Today's wooden roller coaste. 'though strong, have been made to look and sound like the old ones. One of these is the Texas Cyclone in Houston, Texas which was built to look like the Coney Island Cyclone. However, it is bigger and faster.

The metal roller coasters look stronger and safer than the wooden ones. They are quieter, too, but can be even more frightening. They make huge loops and double turns very high up in the air. They go very fast, and the passengers are often turned upside down. The Python, one of the metal roller coasters with a double turn, is at Busch Gardens in Tampa, Florida.

1. Roller coasters are enjoyed by
   a. some people.
   b. all people.
   c. children only.
   d. athletes only.

2. The writer tells about
   a. old-fashioned wooden roller coasters.
   b. modern wooden roller coasters.
   c. modern metal roller coasters.
   d. various kinds of roller coasters.

3. We can conclude that riders who would least enjoy roller coasters are those who have
   a. a good sense of humor.
   b. weak stomachs.
   c. steady nerves.
   d. a desire for fun.

4. We can conclude that roller coasters are popular
   a. in the West.
   b. in the North.
   c. in the South.
   d. all over the United States.

Passage 6

In 1942, 19 years before John F. Kennedy became president of the United States, he was a war hero.

During World War II, Kennedy was in command of a boat called PT-109. A PT boat is a small boat with torpedoes.

PT-109 was on duty off the Solomon Islands in the Pacific Ocean. One night Kennedy's boat was cut in half by a Japanese destroyer. Two men were killed, one man was burned, and Kennedy's back was hurt.

The men who lived hung on all night to the part of the boat that was still floating. The next day they swam for five hours to get to an island. Although he had bad back pains, Kennedy pulled the burned man along. They were in the water for 15 1/2 hours.

When they got to the island, they were cold, wet, and hungry. For the next few days Kennedy swam from island to island for help. At last he found friendly people. They took a letter that was written on a coconut husk asking for help. On the sixth day the Americans were rescued.

Kennedy was given the Navy and Marine Corps medal for bravery. Because he was wounded, he was also given the Purple Heart.

Passage 6

1. Kennedy and his men
   a. swam to an island the next day.
   b. were saved by a seaplane.
   c. hung on to a boat until help came.
   d. got to an island in a life boat.

2. On the island Kennedy asked for help by using
   a. a radio.
   b. a telephone.
   c. a coconut husk.
   d. a palm leaf.

3. Kennedy was a hero because he
   a. was in command of a PT boat.
   b. risked his life to save his men.
   c. fought the Japanese.
   d. hurt his back.

4. We can conclude that Kennedy was
   a. brave.
   b. shy.
   c. selfish.
   d. weak.

Passage 7

The Chicago Fire of 1871 was the worst disaster of the 19th century.

The fire is said to have started one evening in Mrs. O'Leary's barn on the West Side of Chicago. Several hours after she milked her cow, it kicked over a kerosene lamp, and the cow started the fire. We do not know if the story is true, but we do know that the fire began in a barn on the West Side.

The fire spread rapidly because of the wooden buildings, a strong wind, and a dry season. The fire lasted 27 hours and spread to all parts of the city. Other cities sent 25 fire companies to help put out the fire. Federal troops were also used to help fight the fire and keep order, too. At last rain put out the fire.

There was a lot of damage. 90,000 people were left homeless, and 18,000 buildings were destroyed. Property damage was almost 200 million dollars. In addition, about 300 people died.

People from all over the world helped Chicago by sending food and clothing. Within a month 4,000 two-room cottages had been built to house people. In a few years, Chicago was completely rebuilt.

1. The best title for this passage is
   a. Mrs. O'Leary's Cow.
   b. The Year 1871.
   c. A Kerosene Lamp.
   d. A Terrible Fire.

2. Choose the best answer.
   Which parts of the city were hurt by the fire?
   a. the West Side
   b. the South Side and the East Side
   c. the North Side
   d. all sides

3. People who stayed in Chicago after the fire showed
   a. courage.
   b. fear.
   c. weakness.
   d. laziness.

4. What helped to start and to end the fire?
   a. a cow
   b. firemen
   c. the weather
   d. carelessness

Passage 8

In June, 1978 a moon, which is a natural satellite, was found circling the planet Pluto.

By chance, James Christy, a scientist, spotted the moon. He saw it while looking at photos of Pluto. This new moon is called 1978-P-1. Mr. Christy, though, wants its permanent name to be Charon.

Pluto is the most distant of the planets and is one of the least known. It is 2.8 billion miles from the earth. Compared to other planets, it is small.

After studying Charon, scientists think that Charon and Pluto could be called double planets. Charon is large. It is between one-third and one-half the size of Pluto. Its orbit is very near Pluto's and through a telescope they seem to be one object.

In the past, scientists thought that Pluto's gravity disturbed the orbits of the two planets closest to it, Uranus and Neptune. After finding Charon, though, they feel that Pluto is too light to do this. Now they think that there must be large objects beyond Pluto's orbit. They feel that there might even be a new planet. Perhaps this unknown mass is disturbing the orbits of its two neighboring planets.

1. Charon is
    a. a newly discovered planet.
    b. a newly discovered moon.
    c. a star.
    d. the first known moon.

2. Charon's discovery is important because it
    a. is proof that there are no large objects beyond Pluto.
    b. shows that Pluto is disturbing the earth's orbit.
    c. shows that Pluto is too small to be a planet.
    d. proves that new moons can be discovered.

3. Mr. Christy must feel
    a. sorry that he didn't find Charon sooner.
    b. very proud of his discovery.
    c. that he is smarter than other scientists.
    d. embarrassed by all the publicity.

4. Who would know the most about Charon?
    a. students
    b. scientists
    c. doctors
    d. teachers

Passage 9

Thomas A. Edison lived from 1847 to 1931. He is known as one of the greatest inventors in the world. His inventions have improved the lives of millions of people. Edison was not afraid to try. Even when he failed with something new, he did not give up.

In 1877 he made the first record player. This talking machine surprised the world. His greatest invention, the electric light, was accomplished in 1879.

Edison also invented the stock ticker, the dictaphone, and the duplicating machine. He also helped in the development of movies. In 1914 he showed that the record player and the camera could be connected to make talking pictures.

Many people and countries honored Edison with awards and medals while he was alive. For example, France appointed him to the Legion of Honor, and the United States Congress awarded him a gold medal for his inventions because he had done so much to improve the lives of so many people.

31 years after he died, his laboratory and his home in West Orange, New Jersey were made a national monument. This monument is called the Edison National Historic Site.

1. Choose the best answer.
   Edison is called the greatest inventor because he invented
   a. the electric light.
   b. the record player.
   c. the stock ticker.
   d. so many useful things.

2. The world honored Edison
   a. only when he was alive.
   b. only after he died.
   c. very little.
   d. while he was alive and after he died.

3. We can conclude that Edison became a great inventor because he
   a. was lucky.
   b. worked very hard on his ideas.
   c. wanted to make money.
   d. had a rich father.

4. We can conclude that Edison was a man who
   a. asked a lot of questions.
   b. never listened to other people.
   c. did not like to read.
   d. liked to go to parties and dances.

Passage 10

The work of circus clowns is more than just fun and games. Clowns have to work to make people laugh. They have to know many tricks and acts.

In the past it was difficult to learn how to be a clown. Today there are special schools called clown colleges which give courses on how to be a clown. The Ringling Brothers, Barnum and Bailey Circus has a program like that. Both men and women can go there to learn acting, acrobatics, dancing, juggling, magic, and tumbling. They also learn the art of makeup.

Clowns have to know how to make up their faces. They try to make their faces different from those of other clowns. They paint their faces with clown white and grease paint, and they use special eye make-up. Some even attach false noses to their faces.

Clowns own many different costumes and wigs. They have shoes and stockings to match. They change their costumes to fit in with their acts. They also change them to fit in with the seasons of the year and important holidays.

Successful clowns have to like people, both children and grownups. They have to enjoy making people laugh.

Passage 10

1. The best title for this passage is
   a. Today's Clowns.
   b. Clowns of the Past.
   c. Clowns' Costumes.
   d. What Good Clowns Should Know.

2. It is easier for young people to become clowns today than it was 50 years ago because
   a. older clowns are more willing to teach them.
   b. more clowns are needed.
   c. costumes cost less.
   d. clown schools give good courses.

3. The best clowns are those who
   a. are funny-looking.
   b. are silly.
   c. give away balloons.
   d. have learned how to entertain people.

4. We can conclude that clowns
   a. have an easy life.
   b. work hard.
   c. are stupid.
   d. dislike their work.

Passage 11

The story of pretzels is an interesting one. The pretzel was invented over 1,100 years ago by a monk in Europe. He twisted a strip of leftover dough. He shaped the dough to look like children's arms folded in prayer and called it *pretiola*. This is a Latin word which means "little rewards." He gave these twists to children as gifts when they learned their prayers. In later years this word became the word *pretzel*.

For hundreds of years pretzels were made of soft dough and sold in Europe. These soft pretzels could be kept for a short time only. Then hard pretzels were baked. People liked their taste and the fact that they could be kept for months.

When Europeans came here, they brought the art of making pretzels with them. Usually pretzels were baked in homes in open-hearth fires.

The first commercial pretzel bakery was opened in 1861 in Lititz, a small town in Pennsylvania. Our country's big pretzel business grew out of this small bakery. Now over 490 million pounds of pretzels and pretzel products are produced each year in the United States. There are about nine different types of pretzels which come in a wide variety of shapes and sizes.

1. In Europe pretzels
   a. were never popular.
   b. were eaten only by children.
   c. were popular for about 100 years.
   d. were popular for many hundreds of years.

2. When hard pretzels were invented, people liked them better than soft ones because they
   a. were cheaper.
   b. were easier to bake.
   c. had more vitamins.
   d. could be kept fresh for a longer time.

3. Choose the best answer.
   How did the bakery help the people of Lititz?
   a. It gave work to a few townspeople.
   b. It made the town more beautiful.
   c. It brought money and big business to the town.
   d. It brought a few tourists to the town.

4. Which of the following statements is not correct?
   Pretzels became a big business in America because
   a. large commercial bakeries were built.
   b. machines were used to make pretzels.
   c. many different kinds of pretzels were made.
   d. people like the soft-dough pretzels.

Passage 12

Count Dracula is the most famous vampire in the world. A vampire is a make-believe corpse that comes alive at night and sucks people's blood. Dracula has scared millions of people.

People first heard about this count in the book *Dracula*, written in 1897. In the book he is disguised as a Rumanian count. He plans to conquer England by making its people worship vampires.

The author modeled the count after a Rumanian prince called Dracula meaning son of the devil. This prince lived during the 1400s and was known throughout Europe for his great cruelty.

A tale is told about some Turks who came to see the prince. They refused to take off their turbans. The prince was so mad that he had the turbans nailed to their heads.

After his death people still told tales about him. Children were warned "Be good or Dracula will get you."

Count Dracula was always a popular figure. Many plays were written about him.

In 1921 Germany made the first Dracula horror movie. Ten years later America produced its own Dracula horror film. People liked this film so much that since that time more than 100 Dracula horror movies have been made.

Passage 12

1. Choose the best answer.
   Count Dracula
   a. lived in the 1890s.
   b. is a make-believe character.
   c. spent his life in England.
   d. lived in the 1400s.

2. Vampires are feared because they are said to
   a. be corpses.
   b. suck people's blood.
   c. bite people.
   d. carry disease.

3. Choose the best answer.
   Dracula movies are popular because people
   a. like to be frightened.
   b. are interested in Rumania.
   c. like old movies.
   d. like comedies.

4. Dracula films are important to the movie industry because they
   a. helped make horror films popular.
   b. were the first movies filmed in color.
   c. were especially popular with Germans.
   d. cost less to make.

Passage 13

People think of ice cream as an American food. Yet, ice cream really came from Asia. In the late 1200s Marco Polo, the great explorer, is said to have seen rich Asians eating dishes of ice. Camels had brought the ice from distant mountains. Before it was served, the ice had been flavored with fruits.

Maro Polo brought this new dish to Italy. In France chefs changed the ice recipe and made ice cream.

At first, chefs tried to keep the recipe a secret. They wanted it to be a special dish for rich people. By the late 1700s, though, ice cream was sold throughout Europe and America.

Some great Americans loved ice cream. George Washington was the first to buy a special machine for making it. When Thomas Jefferson returned from France, he brought an ice cream recipe home with him. Dolly Madison, wife of President James Madison, also liked ice cream, and she often served it at the White House. In fact, a famous brand of ice cream was even named after her.

In the late 1800s, the ice cream industry began to grow. A way of keeping ice cream frozen had been found, so ice cream makers did not have to worry about ice cream melting anymore.

Passage 13

1. The best title for this passage is
   a. Some Famous Ice Cream Lovers.
   b. How Ice Cream Became a Well-Known Food.
   c. Dolly Madison Ice Cream.
   d. Ice Cream and Ices.

2. When did ice cream become well-known in many countries?
   a. in the 1200s
   b. in the 1500s
   c. in the 1600s
   d. in the 1900s

3. Who do you think was the most important person in the history of ice cream?
   a. Marco Polo
   b. Dolly Madison
   c. Thomas Jefferson
   d. George Washington

4. What makes it possible for ice cream to be sold everywhere today?
   a. People can afford to buy it.
   b. There are many recipes for it.
   c. It is easy to keep it frozen.
   d. Many people like ice cream.

Passage 14

The Tournament of Roses Parade at Pasadena, California has been an annual New Year's Day event since 1890.

One million people line the five and a half mile route, and about 100 million watch it on TV. It is seen in the United States and in many other parts of the world. The Rose Bowl football game, a famous game between two of the country's best college teams, follows the parade.

Each year the 61 floats in the parade are based around a special theme or idea. Judges choose the most beautiful and original floats, and these receive prizes and awards.

Designing and making the floats take many months. They cost between $50,000 and $250,000 each. A metal or wood frame is built around a stripped-down car, truck, or jeep chassis (SHA-see). The frame is colored. Fresh flowers, mostly roses, are attached from four to forty-eight hours before the parade. Volunteers like to help.

There are many different kinds of floats. Some have real people in or on them while some only have lifelike figures. The viewers enjoy the many scenes. One float may tell a story while another may show a historical event.

22 bands from the United States and other countries march in the parade. Some of the world's best riders and horses are seen.

1. The best title for this passage is
   a. The Rose Bowl Football Game.
   b. Prize-Winning Floats.
   c. A Famous Yearly Parade.
   d. A New Year's Day Celebration.

2. According to this passage, a prize-winning float must have
   a. a good designer.
   b. beautiful artificial flowers.
   c. the latest model car.
   d. live figures.

3. We can conclude that today the Tournament of Roses can be enjoyed by many people because they
   a. can fly to Pasadena to see it.
   b. can watch it on black and white TV.
   c. can watch it on color TV.
   d. can hear about it on the radio.

4. Who would be the best float judge?
   a. a farmer
   b. a mechanic
   c. an artist
   d. a musician

Passage 15

St. Bernard dogs have been helping people for hundreds of years. People first heard about St. Bernards in the year 962 when robbers attacked some pilgrims who were traveling to Rome over the Swiss Alps. The robbers stole their food, and they killed half the group. The survivors came down the mountain into Italy. They told Brother Bernard, a monk, their story. He decided to build a shelter where people could find aid in case of blizzards or robbers.

However, Brother Bernard found that many people never reached the shelter because they were lost or buried in avalanches while crossing the mountains.

The monks then decided to use dogs to help rescue these travelers. They used Swiss hounds who were descendants of Molossus dogs from Asia.

From these hounds the monks developed a breed of dogs with an excellent sense of smell. They can follow human footprints that are days old and go into the deepest drifts to find a lost traveler. The dogs are known as St. Bernards.

Through the years St. Bernards have saved 2,500 lives. They use their own bodies to aid people. The dogs travel in groups of four. When they find a victim, two of the dogs lie down to warm him, one on each side. To revive him another licks his face. The fourth dog runs back to the monks for help.

Today because of modern communication and cars, the dogs are not used as much as they were in past years.

1. St. Bernards have been helping people for
   a. less than 100 years.
   b. less than 500 years.
   c. less than 1,000 years.
   d. over 1,000 years.

2. St. Bernards have
   a. a keen sense of smell.
   b. excellent eyesight.
   c. poor hearing.
   d. little courage.

3. We can conclude that Brother Bernard
   a. liked to travel.
   b. cared about people.
   c. did not care about people.
   d. had little interest in dogs.

4. We would probably not find St. Bernards in
   a. the Swiss Alps.
   b. the Italian Alps.
   c. the Rocky Mountains.
   d. the Sahara Desert.

Passage 16

Helen Keller was a handicapped child who became one of the most famous women in the world. She was born in Alabama in 1880. When she was 19 months old, she had an illness which left her blind and deaf. Because she could not hear, she could not speak.

She developed a bad temper so that when she didn't get what she wanted, she flew into a rage. Her loving parents didn't know what to do, but they did not punish her. They were advised to get a teacher from the Perkins School for the Blind, in Boston. Luckily, they were wealthy and could afford a special teacher.

A 20-year-old girl, who had been blind herself, came to teach six-year-old Helen. Anne Sullivan was a firm, loving, and patient teacher.

Deaf people sometimes learn to talk with their hands and fingers, using certain specially coded gestures. Because Helen could not see, her teacher spelled words into her hand. Helen learned to read by using the Braille system. In Braille, raised dots on the paper stand for letters. She also learned to write.

She learned to speak by feeling the vibrations on her teacher's throat and feeling her lips as she said words.

Helen worked hard. She wanted to be able to read, talk, and write like a normal person. With her teacher's help she graduated with honors from Radcliffe College, a famous college for women.

She spent her long life writing and speaking. She traveled all over the world, and people saw that this blind, deaf woman had demonstrated great courage.

Passage 16

1. This passage tells us that blind people learn to read by
   a. using books with raised dots on the pages.
   b. using the hand alphabet.
   c. listening to records.
   d. feeling vibrations.

2. Helen Keller
   a. died at an early age.
   b. lived a full, useful life.
   c. was afraid to leave the United States.
   d. was interested only in her problems.

3. We can conclude that before they got her a teacher, Helen's parents
   a. were ashamed of her.
   b. were too strict.
   c. didn't know how to handle her.
   d. didn't give her any attention.

4. We can conclude that Helen graduated from college because
   a. her teachers felt sorry for her.
   b. she was not required to take all the courses.
   c. other students did her work.
   d. she worked much harder than students who could see and hear.

Passage 17

The National Air and Space Museum in Washington, D.C. tells about the history of flying and space travel.

There are many famous planes on display there. People can even see *Flyer*, the Wright Brother's plane, which was the first plane to fly successfully. Perhaps the most famous plane in the museum is Charles Lindbergh's *The Spirit of St. Louis*. It flew the first solo, non-stop trip to Europe. One can also see the *Bell X-1* which was the first manned plane to fly faster than the speed of sound. Looking at the *Bell X-1* one realizes how much flying grew from those first early planes.

The museum has early fighter planes as well. There are planes from World Wars I and II. There is also a display of a World War I airstrip in France. People can see French and German World War I planes, and they can even hear men discussing a flying mission.

People can board a World War II aircraft carrier. Films show the sea rolling and planes soaring into the sky. A bomber and fighter plane are aboard the carrier.

Space travel is explained in many ways. There are rockets, satellites, and space capsules. There is also a small piece of rock from the moon.

One special exhibit shows the United States and Russian space achievements. Here visitors may enter a large space capsule. It shows what living in space must be like.

Other displays show passenger planes, private planes, balloons, and helicopters.

1. The museum shows people how
   a. planes have developed.
   b. planes are made.
   c. planes are flown.
   d. expensive flying is.

2. Which statement is correct?
   a. The museum has only famous planes.
   b. The museum has a small display on space travel.
   c. Fighter planes are the most popular display.
   d. Many types of flying machines are shown.

3. We can conclude that the people who set up the museum showed
   a. little imagination.
   b. some imagination.
   c. no imagination.
   d. much imagination.

4. The museum would be liked best by people interested in
   a. World War I.
   b. naval history.
   c. World War II.
   d. flying.

Passage 18

Blue jeans were invented by Levi Strauss over 100 years ago. During the 1850s he sold supplies to gold miners in San Francisco.

He realized that people needed strong pants for this rough country. He had a large stock of canvas. He had a tailor make a pair of pants from the canvas.

Later, because canvas was hard to dye, the pants were made of denim. Some people started to call these pants "Levi's." Later they were called blue jeans.

During the late 1860s Jacob Davis, a tailor, wrote to Mr. Strauss. He suggested that copper rivets or bolts be put on the pants since they would help to prevent tears. Soon the two men became partners.

Until the 1930s blue jeans were worn only in the West. Then rich easterners started to go West for ranch vacations. They liked to dress up like the cowboys. When their vacations were over, they took their new jeans back home with them.

After World War II, the jeans industry grew even more. New fabrics and styles were developed, and more companies started to make blue jeans. During the 1960s jeans became very popular with young people, and they are still popular today.

Blue jeans have changed little since they were first invented. They are still snug fitting and usually straight-legged. Today, jeans are worn all over the world.

1. Blue jeans have remained popular because they
   a. wear very well.
   b. are beautiful.
   c. are very warm.
   d. are very cheap.

2. Who helped make blue jeans popular all over America?
   a. factory workers
   b. gold miners
   c. rich easterners
   d. tailors

3. We can conclude that both Mr. Strauss and Mr. Davis
   a. were always poor.
   b. were lazy.
   c. were smart.
   d. wore only blue jeans.

4. If you wanted to make the most money, when would be the best time to be in the blue jeans business?
   a. in the 1880s
   b. in the 1920s
   c. in the 1930s
   d. in the 1960s

Passage 19

Gerbils are mouselike rodents. They are very popular pets in the United States, and thousands of people own them. The first ones came to this country in 1954 when Dr. Victor Schwenker, a scientist, brought them here. He wanted to use them for scientific research because they were being used with great success in Japan. Dr. Schwenker got his gerbils from a lab in Japan. These first gerbils were expensive.

Gerbils begin breeding when they are two and one-half to three months old. They can have a litter of up to 12 babies a month. As a result, Dr. Schwenker soon had plenty of gerbils.

The workers in his lab found them friendly and easy to care for. Gerbils do not need any special room temperature. The workers began taking them home. They liked them as pets. Because gerbils sleep at night, they are awake during the day. It is fun to watch them.

Soon pet stores sold gerbils. As they became more common, they cost less.

Sometimes there are problems when strange animals are brought into a country. If they carry any diseases, they can give these diseases to people. Luckily, gerbils do not do this.

However, gerbils multiply quickly. If they escaped, they could destroy farm crops. For this reason California and New Mexico do not allow them into their states.

1. Gerbils were first brought into this country because they
   a. make good pets.
   b. multiply quickly.
   c. are easy to care for.
   d. were wanted for research.

2. The best title for this passage is
   a. Dr. Schwenker.
   b. Research Animals.
   c. Pets.
   d. Gerbils in the United States.

3. Gerbils are disliked by many farmers because they
   a. spread disease.
   b. damage farm tools.
   c. eat crops.
   d. attack farm animals.

4. Choose the best answer.
   The most important reason for giving a gerbil as a pet to a young child is that they
   a. breed very young.
   b. are easy to care for.
   c. produce big litters.
   d. are cheap.

Passage 20

White sharks are called "man-eater" sharks. They are seen in seas that have warm temperatures. Migrating with the seasons, they travel away from the tropics in the summer and return there in the winter.

The white shark is the third largest shark and the third largest fish in the world. Most are between 8 and 15 feet long. However, 20-foot and even 36-foot sharks have been measured.

Their bellies are always white, but their body coloring varies. It can be gray, brown, blue, or white.

Shaped like torpedoes, their bodies are made for speed. Their strong tails move them quickly through the water. Their speed is a great help to them when they attack their prey.

Their teeth also help them. They have 50 sharp, saw-edged teeth. Like other sharks they have several rows of teeth, one behind the other.

Their mouths are so wide that they can often eat their prey whole. Sea lions, seals, and even other sharks have been found whole in their stomachs. In addition, white sharks eat almost all kinds of invertebrates, fish, and mammals.

The white shark has attacked more people than any other shark, but these attacks are very rare. The worst attack happened in 1916 off the coast of New Jersey. A white shark killed four people and badly hurt a fifth person. Later the shark was caught and killed.

1. White sharks are famous because
   a. they are smart.
   b. they have excellent hearing.
   c. their coloring is very beautiful.
   d. they sometimes attack people.

2. What is most important to sharks?
   a. their shape
   b. their size
   c. their stomachs
   d. their coloring

3. Which of these could be a full-grown white shark?
   a. a 12-foot blue-bellied shark
   b. a 4-foot white-bellied shark
   c. a 14-foot gray-bellied shark
   d. a 15-foot white-bellied shark

4. We can conclude that people remember shark attacks because
   a. they happen so often.
   b. they happen so rarely.
   c. they are so terrible when they do happen.
   d. people are interested in sharks.

Passage 21

Parrots were kept as pets over 2,000 years ago by rich people in Greece and Rome. Explorers brought parrots to North America about the year 1600.

People are amazed when they hear parrots talk or see them do tricks. They can see these tropical birds in zoos, bird sanctuaries, and some pet shops. Parrots are the most popular cage birds.

There are many different kinds of parrots—over 300 species. They are various sizes, shapes, and colors. Many have brilliant colored feathers. Most parrots have large heads and thick, hooked bills. They have strong feet, which they use as people do their hands.

They are liked as pets because they are as friendly as puppies. They seem almost like human beings. A healthy parrot lives as long as a healthy person lives.

Some parrots can be taught to repeat sounds and words, and they can even learn to count. They can also be taught playful acts and tricks like the following: roller skating, skate boarding, riding tiny bicycles or riding on toy carousels. A parrot can even shoot a toy cannon, making another parrot "fall dead."

The price of a parrot depends on what type of parrot it is. A good talking bird costs at least $1,200. A rare species costs about $10,000.

All parrots bought in the United States must be bred here. They are an endangered species and, thus, cannot be imported to the United States.

1. Choose the best answer.
   Parrots
   a. are always alike.
   b. differ only in color.
   c. differ a great deal.
   d. can be seen only in tropical countries.

2. Choose the best answer.
   The main reason that parrots are popular as pets is that they
   a. have strong feet.
   b. show love for their owners.
   c. are clean birds.
   d. are beautiful birds.

3. According to this passage parrots usually die when they are about
   a. 1 to 10 years old.
   b. 11 to 20 years old.
   c. 21 to 30 years old.
   d. 60 to 80 years old.

4. Choose the best answer.
   A person starting a parrot shop
   a. needs little money.
   b. needs a lot of money.
   c. must love reptiles.
   d. does not need to know anything about parrots.

Passage 22

A dirigible is a light airship that looks like a huge balloon. The *Hindenburg* was the largest airship ever made. In 1937 it flew from Germany to the United States and suddenly burst into flames over New Jersey.

The *Hindenburg* was the pride of Nazi Germany. The ship was 804 feet long and could travel 8,000 miles non-stop. It could carry 97 passengers and 61 crew members. On this particular flight, the ship had 36 passengers, and they had paid 400 dollars for their one-way flight.

Just as the ship was about to land there was a large explosion. A great burst of flames rose from the tail. The ship was ripped in two. Many people fell or jumped to the earth. To save themselves some of the crew tried to grab the guide ropes, but they missed and fell to their death.

American marines and sailors were waiting for the ship. They tried to catch the falling people. When the burning ship landed, they jumped into it to see if they could save more people. Sadly, 36 people died.

Usually helium keeps an airship in the air, which is safer because helium cannot catch fire. The *Hindenburg*, though, carried hydrogen gas, which catches fire easily.

No one knows why this tragedy happened. A spark from the engine might have set the gas on fire. Some people feel the fire was the result of sabotage. Many people wanted to see Nazi Germany's ship destroyed.

1. People in Germany were proud of the *Hindenburg* because it was
   a. the biggest dirigible ever made.
   b. the first dirigible ever made.
   c. the biggest plane ever made.
   d. the fastest plane ever made.

2. What might have caused the *Hindenburg* to explode?
   a. helium
   b. hydrogen gas
   c. a collision
   d. poor weather

3. When the *Hindenburg* exploded, American sailors and marines showed
   a. little interest.
   b. much fear.
   c. great courage.
   d. great joy.

4. We can conclude that travel on the *Hindenburg* was
   a. comfortable because there was a large crew.
   b. not comfortable because there were too many passengers.
   c. not comfortable because there was a small crew.
   d. not comfortable because it took too long.

Passage 23

Emma Lazarus will always be remembered for a poem that she wrote in 1883 that is written on the pedestal of the Statue of Liberty in New York harbor.

Emma Lazarus was a young New York author. She was asked to write a poem for a raffle to raise money to build a pedestal for the Statue. She refused to write one because she did not like the Statue. She thought it was too big.

A rich young woman who had gone to private schools, Emma Lazarus was interested in books and writers and knew little about the poor people who were coming to America to seek freedom.

Then one day she saw a shipload of 250 men, women, and children who were waiting to come into the United States. They were Russian Jews who had been forced to flee because of their religion. Although most of them had nothing but the clothes they wore, they were happy that they had not been killed and had reached America's shores safely. They were looking forward to a new life in a new land.

When Emma Lazarus saw them, her feelings changed. She thought of the thousands in the Old World who also wanted to come to the New World. Then she realized how much hope the Statue would give these people, so she changed her mind. She decided that she wanted to write a poem for them. She called her poem *The New Colossus.*

1. Emma did not want to write a poem about the Statue of Liberty because she thought
   a. it was too small.
   b. it was ugly.
   c. she was in Europe.
   d. she could not write poems.

2. In the 1880s the main reason that people came to America was:
   a. They liked to travel.
   b. They were looking for freedom.
   c. They were rich but thought they could make more money here.
   d. They wanted to visit their American relatives.

3. From this passage we can conclude that people's opinions can be changed by what they
   a. see.
   b. are told by friends.
   c. read in books.
   d. hear in speeches.

4. We can conclude that Emma Lazarus
   a. was rich and silly.
   b. was rich but not well educated.
   c. was rich and kind hearted.
   d. was always interested in both rich and poor people.

Passage 24

Lippizan horses are often compared to ballet dancers since they, too, are known for their grace and strength.

The Lippizan breed began in the 1500s. Maximilian, the emperor of Austria, felt that his knights needed a riding school like the one he had seen in Spain. He wanted horses for his school that would be beautiful in peace and strong in war. He bred Arab stallions with Spanish mares, and white Lippizans were the result.

The emperor founded the Spanish Riding School of Vienna. This school has used Lippizans since the emperor's time. The horses are given special training. Then they are shown in fantastic horse shows at the school. People come from all over the world to watch. They see horses make great leaps with their hind legs held under their stomachs. They gasp as horses spring six feet into the air and push their hind legs out.

Lippizans take a long time to grow. Most horses are racing when they are two. Lippizans, though, stay with their mothers until they are four. Then they start training, but they are not saddled until they are five. At six the real training starts, and they are taught the ballet movements for which they are famous.

Only stallions are trained. The mares are not strong enough to perform the ballet movements. They are used only for breeding.

1. Lippizan horses are famous for their
   a. size.
   b. speed.
   c. temper.
   d. grace.

2. The Lippizan breed began because Maximilian wanted
   a. horses that would be brave in war.
   b. to compete with the king of Spain.
   c. a breed of only white horses.
   d. horses that would be strong and beautiful.

3. At what age would a Lippizan horse give his best performance?
   a. two years
   b. four years
   c. five years
   d. eight years

4. The Lippizan breed is about
   a. 100 years old.
   b. 200 years old.
   c. 300 years old.
   d. 400 years old.

Passage 25

Susan B. Anthony fought for women's rights. More than any other person she was responsible for women winning the right to vote in this country.

Susan B. Anthony was born in New York in 1820. At first she taught school, but she grew tired of it after a while. She then decided to run her parents' large farm instead.

When she was 30, she met a leader of the women's rights movement. This group thought that women should be allowed to vote. Susan was impressed with their beliefs.

Two years later Susan went to a large political meeting. She was not allowed to speak because she was a woman. After this she said that to be truly respected a woman must be able to vote and own property.

The women's movement became the most important part of Susan's life. She became active in politics because she was a great organizer. Susan went across the country forming women's groups. These groups fought locally for their right to vote. They also wanted to have the same education as men. They thought that all jobs should be open to women as well as men.

When she was young, men made fun of Susan. They said that she fought for women's rights because she was too ugly to find a husband. As an older woman, though, she was greatly admired.

In 1920, 14 years after her death, women in the United States finally won the right to vote.

1. Anthony became active in the women's rights movement when she was
   a. in her 20s.
   b. in her 30s.
   c. in her 40s.
   d. in her 60s.

2. She got new members for the women's rights movement
   a. by putting ads in newspapers.
   b. by having political dinners.
   c. by organizing groups of women.
   d. by speaking on radio and TV.

3. According to this passage, Susan B. Anthony
   a. had a good sense of humor.
   b. was a determined woman.
   c. was easily impressed.
   d. had many different interests.

4. We can conclude that after they got the vote,
   a. all women were completely satisfied.
   b. all women lost interest in politics.
   c. some women wanted to continue to fight for other rights that men had.
   d. many women lost interest in their families.

Passage 26

Karl Wallenda was the most famous high-wire walker in circus history. Sadly, he was killed in 1978. While he was walking on a 75-foot cable strung between two buildings, a gust of wind made him lose his balance.

Karl was born into a circus family in Germany in 1905. His father was a catcher in a flying trapeze act. As children Karl and his brother performed acrobatic stunts in front of restaurants, and people threw money in a hat for them.

While he was still a boy, he joined a high-wire act. At 17 he was so good that he had his own act.

When Karl was 20, he created the first high-wire pyramid act. Circus fans loved it! With his family, the Great Wallendas, he toured the world with it.

His masterpiece was the seven-person pyramid. Only the Wallendas ever performed it. The act was three rows high. Four men were in the first tier. Two men stood above them. Then a woman stood on a chair above the two men.

Some years later tragedy struck. A nephew, who was making his first appearance, could not hold on to the wire long enough. The nephew and Karl's son-in-law were killed. Karl's son was paralyzed. Though the Wallendas continued their act, the seven-tier pyramid was never performed again. In 1972 another son-in-law was killed on his way up to the high wire.

Despite these deaths Karl still loved to perform. He refused to use a net. He often said, "I feel better up there than I do down here. It is my whole life."

Passage 26

1. Karl's most famous act was
   a. the nine-person pyramid.
   b. the seven-person pyramid.
   c. the triple somersault.
   d. the flying trapeze.

2. The Great Wallendas' success was spoiled by
   a. sickness.
   b. accidents.
   c. circus fires.
   d. loss of audience interest.

3. Karl became famous because of his
   a. skill in balancing.
   b. speed.
   c. imagination.
   d. good looks.

4. One difference between a new high-wire walker and an experienced high-wire walker is
   a. natural balance.
   b. strength on the wires.
   c. interest in their job.
   d. courage.

Passage 27

Alison Oldland, an Englishwoman, had her life changed when she adopted a dog that could not make the grade in her local guide dog-training school. To thank the school for the dog Ms. Oldland gave a lecture on art to raise money for the guide-dog school. After her talk, a blind listener asked her to record other talks on art. He told her that it would mean a great deal to him to be able to speak about painting even though he was blind.

Soon Ms. Oldland began meeting with a group of art historians and blind people. Together they started the Living Paintings Trust. This non-profit organization lends albums of 3 dimensional diagrams of artworks to blind people.

Volunteers put together the boxed albums. If a blind person wants to borrow an album, the person calls or sends a letter to the foundation.

The album comes with ten paintings and an accompanying cassette tape. Each album consists of something the trust calls *thermoform*, which are three-dimensional raised plastic sheets. These sheets are made from molds created by three woodcarvers and a sculptor. To people who can see, the thermoforms look like somewhat crude copies of the originals. Ms. Oldland says that they are only diagrams and are not meant to be a work of art. Each thermoform comes with a 15 to 20-minute discussion of the painting and a postcard of the original work for use by a sighted friend.

These albums are designed for use by blind people at home. Of the nearly one million people with visual impairments in Britain, about half have difficulty getting around and rarely go out.

One 60-year-old woman who has been visually impaired all her life said that exploring the albums is like "being loaned someone's eyes for the afternoon."

Passage 27

1. Thermoforms help a blind person to enjoy art more because they allow the person to appreciate the painting
   a. by using the sense of touch.
   b. by using the sense of smell.
   c. by using the sense of sight.
   d. by using the sense of hearing.

2. What is most needed to make a thermoform interesting and informative to a blind person?
   a. the postcard
   b. the tape
   c. discussing the tape with a friend
   d. going to a lecture about the painting

3. What was the major result of Ms. Oldland adopting a dog?
   a. She adopted a lonely animal.
   b. She bettered the lives of many blind people.
   c. She enjoyed the dog's companionship.
   d. Many people got well-paying jobs as volunteers.

4. One can conclude that Ms. Oldland is
   a. sympathetic.
   b. wealthy.
   c. easy-going.
   d. opinionated.

Passage 28

Roberto Clemente is remembered as a great baseball player and a generous man.

Roberto was born in Puerto Rico in 1934. As a child he loved baseball and played for hours. He threw balls against the walls of his room and tried to catch them.

In high school he played shortstop on the school team. He was a track star, too. When the Brooklyn Dodgers held tryouts in Puerto Rico, Roberto was offered a contract. He waited a year, though, to sign it because he wanted to finish high school.

Roberto was sent to a Dodgers farm team in Montreal. He was unhappy there and played poorly.

At the end of the year, the Pittsburgh Pirates drafted him. After a weak first year Roberto became a great fielder and hitter. During his career he became the 11th person to get 3,000 hits in the major leagues. Twice he was given the National League's Most Valuable Player Award. His great fielding won him the Golden Glove for fielding 12 years in a row.

Off the field Roberto spent a lot of time helping others. He visited the sick in hospitals, and he helped kids with sports.

In 1972 Nicaragua was hit by a great earthquake. Roberto started a drive to collect food and clothes for the victims. On New Year's Eve he flew to Nicaragua to deliver these supplies. Shortly after take-off his plane crashed, and Roberto and the four other passengers were killed.

1. During his career Roberto was
   a. traded often.
   b. recognized as an excellent player.
   c. disliked by the fans.
   d. always happy.

2. Who gave Roberto his first big chance?
   a. his high school coach
   b. his college teammates
   c. the Brooklyn Dodgers
   d. the Pittsburgh Pirates

3. Roberto cared
   a. only about himself.
   b. only about his family.
   c. only about Puerto Ricans.
   d. about people all over the world.

4. Probably Roberto was especially popular in
   a. Brooklyn.
   b. Puerto Rico.
   c. Montreal.
   d. Cleveland.

Passage 29

Mummies are bodies of people who died thousands of years ago in Egypt. They fascinate people because they tell us a lot about ancient Egypt. Mummies were first found in 1798. Many of them were taken out of Egypt, but now the government forbids people to do this.

These bodies were preserved by removing the fluids from them. Egyptians did this because they wanted to preserve a dead person's identity after death.

At first, mummies were made naturally. About 5,000 years ago Egyptians buried their dead in the sand. This warm sand dried the bodies, and natural mummies were the result.

Later on, Egyptians feared grave robbers so they buried the bodies in closed tombs. They had to learn how to make their own mummies. It was a long process that took about 70 days. The last step was wrapping the body in linen.

Then the dead person's family and friends had a great feast. They believed that after the feast the body would go on a long trip. They thought that it would go through the underworld to the Judgment Hall. If the person had been good, he would go to a heaven that looked much like Egypt.

People wanted the dead to feel at home so they painted their tombs with happy scenes and put food, drink, and furniture in them. Gold was even placed in the tombs of the rich people.

1. Egyptians made dead people into mummies because it
   a. was the law.
   b. helped prevent disease.
   c. was a quick way to bury the dead.
   d. preserved the bodies.

2. Ancient Egyptian tombs were like
   a. homes.
   b. museums.
   c. churches.
   d. modern graves.

3. Choose the best answer.
   How long did it take to make a mummy?
   a. about a month
   b. about two months
   c. about three months
   d. about four months

4. We can conclude that ancient Egyptian funeral ceremonies were
   a. long.
   b. cheap.
   c. short.
   d. simple.

Passage 30

A volcano is a crack in the earth from which hot rock called lava is forced out. This lava may be liquid or solid. A volcano often erupts with great force, and poisonous gases escape with the lava. The volcanic explosion may look like a ball of fire. When the lava cools, it hardens, and sometimes volcanic mountains are formed. Some volcanoes are thought to be extinct when they have been quiet for hundreds of years. Others are called dormant because they have been quiet for a long time but are still expected to be active again at some point.

In 1902 Mt. Pelee, a volcano on Martinique which is an island in the West Indies, erupted. It had last erupted in 1851 and was thought to be dormant. When it erupted in 1902, the nearby city of St. Pierre was destroyed, and 30,000 people were killed. A man who was a prisoner in an underground dungeon was the only person saved.

In 1990, Mt. Pinatubo in the Philippines erupted many times over a two-week period. Columns of ash and smoke blew 12 miles high into the air. 101 people were killed; hundreds of people were missing, and hundreds of thousands of people were left homeless. Mr. Pinatubo's last major eruption before 1990 was in the year 1380. Just how soon it will erupt again is uncertain.

Scientists are studying volcanoes closely. If they could predict their eruptions, they could prevent terrible losses of life and property.

1. Choose the best answer.
   Volcanoes can be
   a. active.
   b. dormant.
   c. extinct.
   d. active or extinct or dormant.

2. When Mt. Pelee erupted,
   a. everybody in St. Pierre was killed.
   b. one man was saved.
   c. some of the buildings were destroyed.
   d. a few of the buildings were destroyed.

3. We can conclude that scientists are
   a. always able to predict when volcanic eruptions will occur.
   b. never really able to predict when volcanoes will erupt.
   c. studying volcanoes once in a while.
   d. often able to predict when volcanoes will erupt.

4. Choose the best answer.
   We can conclude that volcanoes are feared by people
   a. all over the world.
   b. in the United States.
   c. in the West Indies.
   d. who are cowards.

Passage 31

Bobby Orr was a famous ice hockey player whose special talent in sports ran in his family. His grandfather was a professional soccer player in Ireland, and when he later moved to Canada, he became a hockey player. Orr's father was also a great hockey player. He was asked to try out for a Boston Bruins' farm team. However, he turned the offer down because World War II had started, and Doug Orr joined the navy.

Bobby Orr learned to skate when he was three. By the time he was four, he was a good skater.

Later, he played defense in a boys' ice hockey league. He was young and small, but the coach thought that for his age he was the best defenseman he had ever seen.

When Bobby was 12, he joined the Parry Sound Bantam hockey team, which beat everyone in the area. The team was then asked to play in the All-Ontario Bantam Championship games. They lost the game, but Orr played terrific hockey. Scouts from the Boston Bruins saw him play, and they were very impressed.

When Bobby Orr was 14, he began to play for the Oshawa Generals, a Bruins farm team in a Junior-A league. Most of the players were 16 to 18 years old, yet Bobby Orr was the best defenseman in the league.

When he was 18, he began playing for the Boston Bruins. His years of training had paid off, and he became an outstanding rookie in the major leagues.

1. The main idea of this passage is
   a. the importance of junior hockey teams.
   b. the importance of the Bantam Championship games.
   c. Orr's rookie years in the Major Leagues.
   d. Orr's development as a hockey player.

2. Orr's family
   a. was talented in sports.
   b. liked soccer better than hockey.
   c. thought Orr should play for a Canadian team.
   d. thought Orr should finish school before playing pro hockey.

3. We can conclude that
   a. one can learn hockey late in life.
   b. it is easy to become a pro hockey player.
   c. hockey and soccer are closely related sports.
   d. training in sports should be started when children are very young.

4. Choose the best answer.
   To become a professional athlete one needs
   a. a lot of money.
   b. an interest in all sports.
   c. years of training.
   d. an athletic family.

Passage 32

George Washington Carver was born a slave, yet he died a great scientist.

He was born in Missouri in 1860. When he was a baby, his parents died. He was raised by the Carvers, the family his mother had worked for.

No blacks were allowed to go to the neighborhood school, but George really wanted to learn. Thus, when he was ten, he left the Carvers. He lived in several towns where he was allowed to go to school. He supported himself by cooking and doing laundry.

In 1896 Carver graduated from Iowa State College. Two years later he earned a master's degree in farm studies. He was then the best trained black farm expert in the country.

Carver had always wanted to help his people so he decided to teach at Tuskegee Institute, a black college in Alabama. Besides teaching he did a lot to help neighborhood farmers, both black and white. Because many farmers could not read, he started a special farm where they could see new farming methods. He also started a traveling farm school.

His work with peanuts made him famous. He was against the South's raising only one big crop, cotton. He urged farmers to plant peanuts. To boost the sale of peanuts he invented 300 different products made from them. He also developed the sweet potato and invented over 200 products made from it.

George Washington Carver was a pioneer in finding new uses for farm crops.

1. George Carver is remembered for his work with
    a. grain.
    b. tobacco.
    c. peanuts.
    d. sugar.

2. Carver went to Tuskegee Institute to
    a. earn more money.
    b. help black people.
    c. help farmers.
    d. live in a warmer climate.

3. We can conclude that as a child he showed
    a. laziness.
    b. selfishness.
    c. ambition.
    d. fear.

4. We can conclude that he was always
    a. bright.
    b. fun-loving.
    c. happy.
    d. friendly.

Passage 33

When skateboarding started in the mid-1960s, skateboards were made of wood and had clay wheels. Since the wheels did not grip concrete well, riders could do very few tricks with them. Soon people lost interest in the sport.

In 1973, though, a new wheel was invented in California. It was made of a plastic called urethane. A skateboard with these wheels moved very quickly, and it also gripped the concrete tightly.

During the next few years skateboards were further improved. The urethane was perfected, and because the boards were shaped better, the rider could do more with them. These skateboards gave a new life to skateboarding.

However, streets were not safe for skateboarding, and good riders found that it was too easy to ride on streets. As a result, skateboard parks sprang up. The first parks were in California and Florida. At first there were only outdoor parks that had concrete slopes with slight curves. Then more exciting parks appeared which had steep descents, banked curves, and vertical walls. Today, there are both indoor and outdoor parks.

In most of these parks the rider must wear a helmet as well as knee and elbow pads. This gear can prevent a fall from causing serious injury.

Whenever they ride, people should always use this safety equipment, and they should learn how to fall safely. Many accidents happen during the first week of riding so it is very important that riders be taught well.

1. Why are the new skateboards popular?
   a. They are safer than the older models.
   b. They are cheaper than the older models.
   c. People can do more tricks with them.
   d. They are better advertised.

2. Skateboard parks developed because
   a. most city parks did not allow skateboarding.
   b. only very good skateboarders could ride on city streets.
   c. parents decided it would be a good idea.
   d. too many accidents happened on streets.

3. The most important rule in a skateboard park is:
   a. Do not smoke.
   b. Leave the park by 7 P.M.
   c. Wear safety equipment.
   d. Take care of your personal property.

4. We can conclude that most parents want their children to
   a. use skateboards with clay wheels.
   b. ride with a partner.
   c. ride in the streets.
   d. ride in skateboard parks.

Passage 34

Wilma Rudolph Ward proved that a person can overcome physical handicaps and become a great athlete.

At the 1960 Olympic Games, she became the first American woman to win three gold medals in track. She ran so well that she was called "Wilma the Wonderful."

Yet, as a child she was severely disabled. At four she had pneumonia and scarlet fever, and the diseases left her with a paralyzed left leg.

Wilma's mother wanted her child to walk. She took her to a hospital in Nashville, Tennessee, which was 45 miles from their home. Doctors said that many years of daily massage might help. Mrs. Rudolph could not afford to take Wilma to the hospital daily so the doctors taught her how to massage the leg. Wilma had many brothers and sisters, and the older ones learned how to do it, too. Wilma had massages a few times a day. She also went to Nashville once a week for treatments.

At six she could limp for short distances. When she was eight, she got a special brace. Then the brace was replaced by a special shoe.

One day Wilma surprised her family by running barefoot in the backyard. Her limp was gone. Two years later Wilma started to run track. In a state meet she won the 50-, 75-, and 100-yard dashes.

Because of her running she received a scholarship to Tennessee State University. Wilma Rudolph Ward set new track records and eventually qualified for the 1960 Olympics.

1. Choose the best title.
   a. A Disabled Person
   b. Running in the Olympics
   c. Conquering a Handicap
   d. A Devoted Family

2. What caused Wilma to become disabled?
   a. an accident
   b. polio
   c. polio and scarlet fever
   d. scarlet fever and pneumonia

3. What can you conclude from this passage?
   a. Nashville doctors were the best in the country.
   b. Everyone who gets scarlet fever and pneumonia becomes disabled.
   c. Mrs. Rudolph was a devoted mother.
   d. Wilma complained a lot about her leg.

4. Why was it a special thrill for Wilma to win Olympic medals? Because she
   a. was an American.
   b. was a woman.
   c. came from a poor family.
   d. had been disabled.

Passage 35

Henry Ford in 1908 produced the first car for the average person, and he called it the Model T. This car was cheap enough to compete with a horse and buggy and was strong enough to run on poor roads. It was so simple that most people could even drive and repair it themselves.

The Model T was sold until 1928. For 20 years half the cars made in the United States were this model.

The Model T was cheaper than other cars because it was not fancy, and it only came in black. In the earlier models, there was no gas gauge or speedometer, and the dashboard had only the ignition key. Rear-view mirrors and windshield wipers were sold as extras.

With better production methods, the time needed to manufacture the car went down from 12 to 1 1/2 hours. As a result, in 1921 the price of the Model T went down from the original 850 dollars to 290 dollars. There were songs and jokes about its low cost. One song was called "You Can't Afford to Marry if you Can't Afford a Ford."

The Model T was hard to run. To start it, the driver had to get out of the car and crank the engine. To fill the gas tank, which was under the driver's seat, the driver had to get out of the car.

Model Ts helped change our nation. Old roads were improved. Gas stations sprang up. The oil and rubber industries grew. More people traveled, and the tourist industry grew, too.

1. People who bought Model Ts did not like
   a. their cost.
   b. their power.
   c. the lack of extra equipment.
   d. the repair bills.

2. To start the Model T the driver had to
   a. push down on the gas.
   b. crank the engine.
   c. turn a key.
   d. push it.

3. Compared to the 1921 Model T, the first Model T was
   a. cheaper.
   b. about three times as much.
   c. about five times as much.
   d. about ten time as much.

4. Because of Model Ts people used more
   a. bicycles.
   b. ships.
   c. horses.
   d. hotels.

Passage 36

Comic books are read all over the world. More than 400 million of them are published each year.

Comic books developed from newspaper comic strips. The first comic book, *Comics on Parade*, came out in 1933. It was made up of old newspaper comic strips and was the size of a magazine. People liked the book so much that it sold out in a weekend.

Detective Comics, a comic book series, came out in 1937. These books were very much like today's comic books. Each had one main idea or figure.

The next year *Superman* came out. It was the most widely read comic of all time. *Captain Marvel*, published in 1939, was the only comic ever to rival *Superman* in sales.

Comic books quickly grew in number. By 1940 there were 60 different comic books, and by 1941 there were 168. These comics had many subjects, but westerns, romance, and science fiction were the most popular.

In the early 1950s, horror and war comics appeared. Some grownups thought they were not fit for children. To fight this type of comic, publishers set up a committee. They tried to control the content and ads in comics. This plan worked until the 1960s, but then some publishers wanted to be free to print violent comics.

Bigger-than-life comic book figures like the *X-Men* and *Spiderman* are popular. Old favorites like *Batman*, *Archie*, and *Superman* continue to be good sellers. Japanese comics are in great demand. European comics are more expensive than American and Japanese comics and generally appeal to an older audience.

Passage 36

1. *Detective Comics* were like present-day comics because they
   a. sold for the same price.
   b. had color pictures.
   c. had one main character or idea.
   d. were magazine size.

2. How long did it take for comic books to become popular?
   a. a few days
   b. five years
   c. 10 years
   d. 40 years

3. We can conclude that people like
   a. action comics the best.
   b. *Archie* comics better than European comics.
   c. many different types of comics.
   d. romance comics the least of all.

4. During the 1950s most comics would probably not have had ads for
   a. toothpaste.
   b. bubblegum.
   c. model cars.
   d. knives.

Passage 37

Jesse Owens was one of the world's greatest runners.

However, as a child he was sickly and weak. His family was poor, and sometimes there was not enough food for everyone.

When Jesse was eight, his parents moved from Alabama to Cleveland, Ohio. They hoped that life would be better there. However, Jesse's father could not find steady work. His mother worked to help raise her eight children, and Jesse had three after-school jobs.

When Jesse was eleven, he met Charles Riley, the track coach for the neighborhood grammar and high school. Riley suggested that Jesse start track because it would build up his thin legs.

Jesse's father encouraged him because he loved track. He had even been county champion in Alabama.

Jesse worked with Coach Riley throughout high school. Coach Riley got him a scholarship to Ohio State which had the best track coach in the country.

Just before his first big college race, Jesse hurt his back. He was in great pain, yet he set world records in the four events he entered.

In 1936 Jesse Owens competed in the Olympic Games in Germany. At that time Adolf Hitler was the ruler of Germany. He thought that black people were not as good as white people, and since Jesse Owens was black, Hitler refused even to shake hands with him. Jesse went on to win four Olympic gold medals. His outstanding Olympic performance showed the world that a person's talents are not based on the color of his/her skin.

Passage 37

1. Choose the best title for this passage.
   a. Running
   b. An Athletic Star
   c. The Life of a Great Runner
   d. Jesse Owens Meets Coach Riley

2. Jesse Owens is usually remembered because of his
   a. college races.
   b. friendship with Coach Riley.
   c. Olympic performance.
   d. high school track record.

3. We can conclude that the most important person in Jesse Owens' track career was
   a. Coach Riley.
   b. his mother.
   c. his Olympic coach.
   d. his father.

4. We can conclude that Jesse's parents
   a. had little interest in their children.
   b. fought often.
   c. had great interest in their children.
   d. were lazy.

Passage 38

Eleanor Roosevelt was called America's First Lady when her husband was president of the United States. Later she was called the first lady of the world because she spent her life trying to help others.

She was born into a rich New York family in 1884. When she was 20, she married her cousin Franklin. They had five children. He was active in politics while she ran the household.

In 1921 her life changed greatly. As a result of polio, Franklin became disabled. To help him she became active in politics.

When her husband became governor of New York in 1929, she acted as his legs. She went to all the places to which he could not go. From these trips she learned how all kinds of people lived.

In 1933 her husband became president. Eleanor traveled all over, and she told Franklin what she saw.

She was shocked by the poverty of the people. Government programs were started to help the poor, and she started her own programs, too. She spoke out on important issues. She urged women to become active in the world, and she criticized laws that were unfair to black people. She used the money she made from her writings and speeches to help people.

After Franklin Roosevelt's death, President Truman made Eleanor Roosevelt a United Nations' delegate. She worked on its Declaration of Human Rights. This historic paper declared the rights of all people.

In her later years she supported many good causes. She was active until her death at the age of 78.

1. When her husband was disabled, Eleanor was forced to
    a. spend more time with her family.
    b. lead a quiet life.
    c. do things she had never done before.
    d. work to support the family.

2. Eleanor Roosevelt
    a. was interested only in politics.
    b. rarely commented on government policies.
    c. spent her last years in retirement.
    d. was interested in many different problems.

3. We can conclude that Eleanor Roosevelt
    a. had a lot of energy.
    b. was an excellent housewife.
    c. had always been interested in politics.
    d. was mainly interested in the United Nations.

4. Who did not like Eleanor Roosevelt?
    People who believed
    a. in government programs for the poor.
    b. in the United Nations.
    c. women should stay at home.
    d. in civil rights.

Passage 39

People often think of baseball as an "all-American" sport, but baseball began and flourished in Spanish-speaking countries just a few years after it started in the United States.

Supposedly the first baseball game was played in Cuba in 1866 when an American ship was docked at Matanzas, a large port in Cuba. The American sailors taught some Cubans how to play the game, and together they built a baseball diamond. By 1874 a number of Cuban baseball teams had been formed, and they played each other on a regular basis. By 1891 there were 75 active teams on the island.

Besides using Cuba for winter and spring training, Cuban baseball teams often served as a training ground for the American major league teams. Before American baseball was integrated in 1947 and black players were allowed in the major leagues, there were about 50 Hispanic-American ballplayers in the major leagues. Some of these players even became members of Baseball's Hall of Fame. After the American teams were integrated, more Hispanic ballplayers of all colors and nationalities became players in the major leagues.

After the Cuban revolution, the flow of players from Cuba to the United States stopped. In 1946 Mexico had established a professional baseball league, and today the Mexican Central League has 14 teams whose gifted young players are often hired by the American major league teams. In the 1970s and 1980s, Hispanic players generally came from the Dominican Republic and Puerto Rico with Venezuela and Mexico also making a strong showing.

Passage 39

1. Choose the best answer:
   a. Baseball is a popular sport worldwide.
   b. Baseball has been played in Cuba for over 150 years.
   c. Cuban baseball came about due to a chance meeting between Americans and Cubans.
   d. By 1900 Cuba had 100 baseball teams.

2. What was the major reason that more Hispanic ballplayers started playing in the major leagues?
   a. The ballplayers wanted to live in the United States.
   b. More foreigners were allowed to settle in the United States.
   c. The color line was broken, and more Hispanic players of all colors and nationalities were hired by major league teams.
   d. Baseball became less popular in Central America so ballplayers came to the United States to work.

3. From this passage we can conclude that
   a. baseball was introduced to Cuba after careful planning.
   b. sometimes a chance meeting can have unexpected results.
   c. a baseball diamond takes a long time to construct.
   d. the number of Mexican baseball teams will remain the same.

4. Choose the best answer:
   Many talented baseball players were not given a fair chance in the
   a. 1930s.
   b. 1950s.
   c. 1970s.
   d. 1990s.

Passage 40

Basketball is the only major sport that has been developed in the United States. In 1891 James Naismith, a physical education teacher at the Young Men's Christian Association (Y.M.C.A.) Training School in Springfield, Massachusetts, was asked to invent a game that could be played between the fall football season and the spring baseball season. Naismith had only one requirement to fulfill: the game had to be played indoors. Winters in Massachusetts were very harsh so any outdoor sport would be very unpopular.

At first he tried to redesign a number of outdoor sports for indoor use, but this was not successful since the sports were not suitable to such a relatively small space. Too many players were getting hurt, and too many windows were being broken. Naismith then decided to devise a non-contact sport in which the players were not allowed to run with the ball. The purpose of the game was two-fold: to shoot a ball into a basket and to stop the other team from doing this.

Naismith asked the janitor to hang a peach basket on the balcony at each end of the gym. Then he divided his eighteen students into two teams and gave them a soccer ball to play with. On a bulletin board he listed the 13 rules of the game. Some people urged him to call this new game *Naismith*, but he decided to call it basketball. In less than a year the game was being played in many parts of the United States as well as Canada. In 1904 the Olympic Games were being held in St. Louis, and basketball was introduced as a demonstration sport. Thus, the game became known worldwide.

1. When James Naismith was told to create a new game,
   a. he could invent any kind of game he wished.
   b. he had to invent a sport that could be played by both men and women.
   c. he was given one important requirement.
   d. he tried to think of a game that could be played year round.

2. Which statement is not true?
   Naismith made basketball a non-contact sport
   a. to avoid players getting hurt.
   b. so school property would not be damaged.
   c. because he was asked to do this.
   d. because a contact sport cannot be played in such a small area.

3. From this passage we can conclude that James Naismith
   a. had a quick-thinking mind.
   b. did not work well under pressure.
   c. was very vain.
   d. preferred outdoor sports.

4. Choose the best answer.
   In the 1890s where could you find people who knew how to play basketball?
   a. Boston and Ottawa
   b. Boston
   c. Paris
   d. London

Passage 41

Cesar Chavez did more than anyone else to improve the lives of migrant farm workers who travel from farm to farm looking for work. Who was Chavez, and what did he accomplish?

Cesar Chavez was born on March 3, 1927 in Arizona and lived on his family's farm. When he was ten, his parents fell behind on their mortgage payments and lost their farm. They moved to California and became migrant workers. Chavez attended 65 elementary schools and never finished high school. After serving in the Navy for two years, he returned home and became a migrant worker. Later he formed the National Farmworkers Association.

Before Chavez organized Mexican-American migrant workers into a union, workers made less than $1.50 an hour. They had no benefits and could not complain if they were treated unfairly.

Chavez used peaceful resistance as a means of fighting. In 1965 he began *La huelga* (the strike) against grape growers in Delano, California. When the strike failed, a nationwide grape boycott began. In 1968 Chavez began the first of his famous fasts. He fasted for twenty-five days to help show how farm workers suffered. A year later 12% of Americans were refusing to buy grapes. Finally in 1970 the growers signed an agreement with the union. Migrant workers got decent pay increases and became qualified for medical insurance and other benefits. Through the union members had a way of challenging employers when they mistreated them. For the first time migrant workers were assured of certain basic worker's rights.

Passage 41

1. The best title for this passage is
   a. *La huelga.*
   b. A Portrait of Cesar Chavez.
   c. Migrant Workers.
   d. The Power of Peaceful Resistance.

2. According to this passage, which statement would Chavez probably not agree with:
   a. Changes can be made through peaceful means.
   b. People have certain basic rights.
   c. Serving in the Armed Forces is a citizen's duty.
   d. By drawing attention to a problem one can help to solve it.

3. One can conclude that Chavez
   a. was a self-educated man.
   b. forgot the experiences of his youth.
   c. believed in the power of the sword.
   d. had faith in the generosity of the grape growers.

4. Who would be Chavez's strongest supporter?
   a. a farmer
   b. a newspaper reporter
   c. a Mexican-American doctor
   d. a Mexican-American worker

Passage 42

Grandma Moses became a famous painter when she was in her 80s. She had always liked painting but did not have time to paint seriously until she was old.

Anna Robertson Moses was born in 1860 and grew up on a farm in New York. When she was six, her father bought her some large pieces of paper to use for drawing. She had only blue chalk, yet she loved drawing. After the paper and chalk were used up, she got red paint from the barn and painted on wood. She also picked berries and used their juices for paint.

When she was only 12, she worked as a maid, and after work she often copied pictures.

Anna married and moved to Virginia. She and her husband had five children. Anna painted only when she made some Christmas cards.

In 1905 the Moses' returned to New York. Their children grew up, and Anna had some free time. She started making pictures out of yarn, but, as she got older, her fingers hurt when she sewed. When she was 70, she started to paint again.

At first, no one noticed her paintings. One day, though, an art collector saw her paintings in a drugstore window. He bought all of them, and he showed them to many people who sold art. Finally, one dealer liked them so much that he showed them in his art gallery. Slowly Grandma Moses' art became well-known. Millions of people loved her colorful paintings of country life, and they paid high prices for her pictures. She painted until her death at 101.

Passage 42

1. Choose the best title for this passage.
   a. An American Painter
   b. A Farm Girl
   c. A Successful Old Artist
   d. A Successful Young Artist

2. Anna became interested in drawing when she was
   a. a child.
   b. a teenager.
   c. a young woman.
   d. an old woman.

3. An important person in Grandma Moses' art career was
   a. her husband.
   b. an art collector.
   c. her children.
   d. her mother.

4. We can conclude that Grandma Moses' old age was
   a. busy.
   b. sad.
   c. quiet.
   d. lonely.

Passage 43

If you plan to take your pet on a trip, prepare ahead of time. At least two weeks before you leave, take your pet to a vet. See if he or she is fit for travel and ask if he or she should have any medicine before leaving. The vet may suggest certain pills for motion sickness or for calming the pet.

Some states or foreign countries have health laws that say animals must have certain injections before they can be admitted. Your vet may have this information. You can also get help on the United States and Canadian laws from a book published by the Department of Agriculture which some libraries have. For information on foreign countries, check with their consulates. You can also ask the airlines on which you are traveling.

Find out if the places where you plan to stay allow pets because many do not.

If you are going by plane or train, ask if pets are allowed. If they are, ask where they will be kept and who will care for them. The big inter-state bus lines in this country do not allow pets.

Choose your pet's carrier carefully. Plastic carriers are better than fiberboard or wooden ones because they can't be chewed.

If going by plane or train during warm weather, try to go in the cooler early morning or evening hours. Also try to avoid very cold winter weather because pets often suffer from extreme cold. Even in your own car, be careful. Do not leave the animal inside with the windows closed because the car may become too hot or too cold.

1. The main idea of this passage is to
   a. warn people to leave their pets at home.
   b. give general information about pet travel.
   c. tell people how to choose their pet carriers.
   d. tell people about foreign pet laws.

2. When taking a pet on a trip, a pet owner
   a. doesn't need to make any special plans.
   b. should stay at friends' homes.
   c. should make plans before leaving home.
   d. should travel by bus instead of plane.

3. We can conclude that
   a. it costs too much to take pets on trips.
   b. some pets may not be well enough to travel.
   c. all train lines treat pets exactly the same.
   d. pets are welcome everywhere.

4. Which person would be the most interested in this passage?
   a. a vet
   b. a pet owner
   c. a motel owner
   d. a pet shop owner

Progress Graph

	1	2	3	4	5	6	7	8	9	10	11	12	13	14	15	16	17	18
4 CORRECT = 100%																		
3 CORRECT = 75%																		
2 CORRECT = 50%																		
1 CORRECT = 25%																		

19 20 21 22 23 24 25 26 27 28 29 30 31 32 33 34 35 36 37 38 39 40 41 42 43

Answer Sheet

Passage	Question 1	Question 2	Question 3	Question 4
1	c	d	a	a
2	c	d	b	c
3	a	d	c	a
4	a	c	a	b
5	a	d	b	d
6	a	c	b	a
7	d	d	a	c
8	b	d	b	b
9	d	d	b	a
10	a	d	d	b
11	d	d	c	d
12	b	b	a	a
13	b	d	a	c
14	c	a	c	c
15	c	a	b	d
16	a	b	c	d
17	a	d	d	d
18	a	c	c	d
19	d	d	c	b
20	d	a	d	c
21	c	b	d	b
22	a	b	c	a
23	b	b	a	c
24	d	d	d	d
25	b	c	b	c
26	b	b	a	b
27	a	b	b	a
28	b	c	d	b
29	d	a	b	a
30	d	b	b	a
31	d	a	d	c
32	c	b	c	a
33	c	d	c	d
34	c	d	c	d
35	c	b	b	d
36	c	a	c	d
37	c	c	a	c
38	c	d	a	c
39	c	c	b	a
40	c	c	a	a
41	b	c	a	d
42	c	a	b	a
43	b	c	b	b